For Conor and Sadhbh
ED and JG

For Kate Janaki (Ella) and Dara Luca
SK

Adam - the facts

The story of Adam (possibly meaning 'red' to symbolize dust from which he was made) is central to the Christian, Jewish and Islamic versions of creation. Many ancient narratives tell of an idealized 'Eden' and the origin of humanity and the universe. Striking parallels can be found in the legends of Babylon, Persia and Greece in particular. Generally accepted as an allegorical tale, literal belief, known as creationism, continues among certain religious groups, in the USA in particular.

The Bible records two versions of creation. *Genesis* ch. 1 (v. 27) states that on the sixth day God created man and woman together: "male and female he created them." In the second chapter (v. 7) woman (Eve) is created later from a rib taken from Adam, "because it is not good that man be alone." Both versions are derived from earlier religious sources, the *Priestly Code* (5th century BC) and the *Jahvist Document* of as early as 800 BC.

The *Koran* records that: "God made you of dust. He said to him 'Be' and he was." Adam's temptation in the Garden of Eden is recorded in both the *Koran* and *Bible*.

Various Adamite cults emerged over the ages. A central part of their philosophy was seeking a return to innocence by applying naturist approaches to prayer and worship. Particularly prominent in Belgium and Holland, the most notable of these groups, the Picards, was exterminated in religious purges during the early 15th century.

Joshua 3:16 mentions Adam as a place where God stopped the flow of the river Jordan to allow the Israelites cross safely into the Promised Land. This record may relate to an actual historical event. In 1927 an earthquake at the same spot halted the flow of the river for almost 24 hours.

A 7th century Irish saint, Adamnan, was reputedly the first person to sight the Loch Ness monster.

He was Abbot of Iona (Scotland), author of a biography on St Colmcille and is still patron saint of the diocese of Raphoe (Ireland).

Adam's Peak, a mountain in Sri Lanka, contains an impression of a human foot at the summit. In Arab tradition, Adam stood on one leg there for up to a 1,000 years in atonement for his crime in Eden.

Our Adam's Apple, more prominent in men, was, according to legend, caused when a piece of 'forbidden fruit' lodged in Adam's throat in the Garden of Eden.

Once there was a boy called Adam. Outside his house there was a large garden. Flowers of every scent, shape and colour bloomed there all year long. The birds sang sweetly from morning until night. Butterflies of yellow and white and blue and red fluttered from shrub to shrub.

If you were very quiet and searched carefully you might see small animals, like a hedgehog sleeping, a mole peeping or a frog hopping.

In Adam's garden the sun shone every day. The air was always warm and still. Adam liked to play in the sun, to listen to the birds, to chase the butterflies and to pick flowers for his table.

When he searched for the small animals, he always made too much noise and they hid silently behind the leaves and branches.

At the end of his garden there were many trees. In spring they had green leaves of every shape and size. Red and black ladybirds lived in the shade. In summer beautiful flowers appeared on their branches. Brown and yellow honeybees danced from tree to tree. In autumn each tree had a different type of delicious fruit. In winter the trees were bare. Adam could see where the birds had built their nests.

Adam's favourite season was autumn, when he ate the fruit from each tree.

There were soft, red berries growing on low bushes which he picked with his hand. Large, black, sugary plums hung down on branches which he plucked by reaching up his arm.

Adam would climb into the low branches of the pear tree to pick its funny shaped, golden fruit. He would climb a little higher to reach the soft, round fruit of the orange tree. Once he climbed onto the lemon tree. It was a very grumpy tree. "Don't climb on my branches," it said crossly. Its oval, yellow fruit looked so nice Adam decided to try it anyway.

What a shock he got! It tasted so bitter he made a face like a chimpanzee! "That will teach you to leave me alone," the grumpy lemon tree said.

At the end of his garden was the largest tree of all. High on its branches were the reddest, juiciest-looking apples you could imagine. Adam had never been able to reach these apples. 'It is dangerous to climb the highest trees,' his mum told him.

One day Adam got bored and decided to climb to the top of the big tree to get the juicy fruit. Up, up, up he climbed. The further he climbed the bigger, redder and juicier the apples looked. Eventually he reached the highest, farthest branch where the biggest apples were. He saw his neighbour cutting the grass. He saw the postman delivering a very heavy parcel. He saw his dog chasing a big, black cat.

Adam stretched out his hand very far to pick the largest apple of all. Just as he touched it, the branch suddenly snapped. With a mighty crash Adam fell from the tree.

Down, down, down he tumbled through the leaves and branches. He hit the ground with a thump. His clothes were torn. His leg was cut. His shoulder was sore and scratched. He had a bump on his head.

When he looked around he realised he had fallen on the nicest flowers and broken them. The noise disturbed the birds and butterflies and they all flew away. Worst of all, the largest, juiciest, red apple had rolled out of view. Adam could not see it anywhere.

'My goodness,' said his mum, as she changed his torn clothes and checked the bump on his forehead, 'now you've learned that there are some things you just shouldn't do.'

Before long Adam was back playing happily in his garden again. Now though, he is content to let the birds pick the fruit on the big red apple tree.

What's in a name?

Usually centuries of history, religious or legendary tradition.

The main source of names is in religious history, in the names of saints (Catherine) and, post Reformation, in the *Bible* and *Old Testament* in particular (Sarah and Adam). The *Koran* provides additional perspective on many of these names.

Names from Celtic legend, like Conor, have recently gained increased attention internationally.

Another source is classical, from pagan, royal or literary figures, e.g. Lawrence (Latin) and Chloe (Greek literature). Historical figures, such as Victoria, also provide a rich source.

Then there's Jack! It probably deserves a category all of its own having appeared from nowhere - but perhaps from Jankin, a version of John - to become the ubiquitous name in fairy tales and now a highly popular first name.

Recently parents have become much more adventurous. This follows the decrease in family and religious bonds that resulted in names passing from generation to generation. Increased access to other cultures has led to 'name globalisation', with names like Tanya, Brooklyn and Chelsea now more popular.